JOHN O'HARA INVITES YOU TO A FAMILY PARTY

"I started to tell you good people how I happened to be making this speech this evening. . . . When we began talking among ourselves about giving a banquet in honor of Sam Merritt we had several discussions about asking somebody prominent like the Governor or maybe some famous doctor or somebody like that. But the more we thought of it the more we wanted to make it what you might call a family party. You won't find anybody here tonight that's a stranger to Sam Merritt."

And no one who reads his story will be a stranger to Sam Merritt. John O'Hara is the son of a small-town Pennsylvania doctor. Perhaps that is why this unusual, affectionate and charmingly told tale has the snap and ring of veracity.
Here is Mr. O'Hara, one of America's great novelists, in a nostalgic and captivating mood.

❦ Published by Bantam Books

JOHN O'HARA
A FAMILY PARTY

A FAMILY PARTY

*A Bantam Book / published by arrangement with
Random House, Inc.*

PRINTING HISTORY

Random House edition published August 1956
2nd printing..........July 1956
3rd printing.....September 1956
4th printing.....November 1956

Published in COLLIERS *August 1956*

Reader's Digest Condensed Books edition published January 1957

Bantam edition published August 1957
2nd printing.......January 1965
3rd printing
4th printing

*Bantam Books are published by Bantam Books, Inc., a subsidiary
of Grosset & Dunlap, Inc. Its trade-mark, consisting of the words
"Bantam Books" and the portrayal of a bantam, is registered in the
United States Patent Office and in other countries. Marca Registrada.
Bantam Books, Inc., 271 Madison Ave., New York 16, New York.*

To Verna Delaney

A Family Party

Stenographic Report

The following is a stenographic report of an address by Mr. Albert W. Shoemaker, president of the Shoemaker Printing Company and former editor and publisher of the Lyons Republican, *at a dinner in honor of Dr. Samuel G. Merritt. The dinner, which took place on September 17, 1955, in the main dining room of the Lyons Hotel, Lyons, Pennsylvania, commemorated the forty years of Dr. Merritt's service to Lyons and surrounding communities and to wish him well upon his retirement from active practice of his profession.*

The affair was sponsored jointly by the Lyons Rotary Club, Kiwanis, Lions, Junior Chamber of Commerce, Patriotic Order Sons of America, Knights of Columbus, Benevolent & Protective Order of Elks, Ancient Or-

der of Hibernians, Knights of Pythias, Ministerial Association, Holy Name Society, Veterans of Foreign Wars, American Legion, Lyons Gun Club, Merchants Association, Boy Scouts of America, Order of the Eastern Star, American Red Cross, Daughters of Isabella, Delphian Society, United Mine Workers of America, and the Nesquehela County Medical Society.

More than two hundred persons, including many prominent in business, labor, industry and the professions, were present at the dinner. The invocation was by the Reverend Father Alexis P. Smirnolinski, pastor of St. Boniface R. C. Church, after which the toastmaster, Mr. Cyril V. Longenecker, introduced several leading out-of-town visitors, who were called upon for brief remarks. They were followed by the address by Mr. Shoemaker, who was the principal speaker of the evening.

The benediction was asked by the Reverend Eustace Muhlenberg Fry, rector of the Lyons Methodist Episcopal Church. Music was provided by the Lyons High School Orchestra under the leadership of Miss Charline K. Smith, B.M.

Mr. TOASTMASTER, Distinguished Guests, Reverend Members of the Clergy, and Ladies and Gentlemen:

Back in February of this year, when a few of us old-timers accidentally discovered that we had in our midst a man who had held the same job for close on to forty years, that seemed such a remarkable accomplishment in these days that a few of us decided we ought to do something about it. This town of ours used to be an important railroad center, before they put in the buses and before the business of mining coal was all shot to—well, a certain place that I understand they have all the coal they need, if the reverend clergy will pardon me.

I mention the railroads because when they were prosperous, one of the greatest honors a

13

man could have was the watch that the rail-road company gave a man when he retired. I used to sometimes wonder why they gave a railroader a watch when he retired instead of when he started out, but of course the rail-roads used to do a lot of things I could never understand, but that's not saying I don't wish we still had them with us. But as I was saying, it was an honor when the company gave a man a watch, and incidentally you never hear of a bus driver bragging about the watch the bus company gave him. Well, be that as it may, the reason why a man was so proud of his watch was because it meant something. It represented something.

What did it represent? It represented that a man had given thirty or forty years of faithful service to his company and to his community, out in all kinds of weather, often performing his duties at the risk of his very life. It represented to one and all that a man had not only done his job and obeyed orders, but oftentimes did that little extra something that meant his train reached its destination on time and without damage to the cargo or injury to the passengers. Railroading was hard work and not only hard work physically. A man had to keep on his toes. If you wanted to go from brakeman to fireman or fireman to engineman, you had to study the rules and pass difficult examinations that if you ever saw the examination for fireman, I wonder how many college graduates could pass it today.

Well, ladies and gentlemen, the more we thought of it the more we decided that we had in our midst a friend of ours who had held a job for forty years, or nearly forty, and while he wasn't a brakeman on the railroad, or a fireman, or an engineman, or for that matter a trackwalker, still he had been serving his community that long, and he was entitled to some recognition. Of course you all know who I am talking about, so I guess I can take the liberty of saying that this old friend of ours, he held his job for forty years. Sure he held his job for forty years. Why? Nobody could fire him.

But seriously, if you want to look at it that way, I'm wrong, because to put it another way, there wasn't a man or woman in Lyons or nearby communities that couldn't fire him. On the railroad there's only a few that can fire you, but this friend of ours, anybody could fire him. But nobody ever did, at least that I know of, so we had to give him credit for keeping his job for forty years with more bosses than anybody I can think of. Not to take anything away from those of you who worked on the railroads, or had fathers or brothers or uncles that were railroaders, but this friend of ours was every bit as important as any engineman or fireman or conductor, and I'm sure some of you will agree with me that maybe he was a little more important. I could look around this room right now and see the faces of some former railroaders that wouldn't be here tonight if it hadn't of been for the friend we are honoring this evening.

And I guess anybody that's old enough can remember how desperately he worked the night of the Short Mountain wreck. That was the time when an 1800-type locomotive ran away and plowed into the Bug loaded with a hundred and eighty miners on their way home from work. For the benefit of the younger ones present, the Bug was the name they gave to the miners' train that took the miners up to Short Mountain and Outerbridge Colliery. They killed fourteen miners not counting members of the crew, and when I was in the Army in France in 1918 I still never saw anything to compare with that rear car of the Bug. They used to back it up to

Outerbridge Colliery, so when the 1800-type ran away she plowed right into that rear car and I don't want to turn your stomachs with a description of the carnage that evening.

I was reporting on my father's newspaper, the good old Lyons *Republican* that I unfortunately couldn't keep its head above water after 1929, and when we heard there was a wreck up on Short Mountain my father sent me up there to cover it, and all I can tell you is that I wish it had been my day off. Only I didn't have a day off. But I wished I had gone for a swim out in the Glen. Anything so I wouldn't have to be there when my father got word about the wreck. We got the word just about as soon as anybody because we used to publish the *Republican* in the building where Hartman's Garage is now, but then it was our office and we had our printing plant there, and of course it was right across the street from the old freight station and down the street from the passenger, and somebody mentioned it to my father and they were making up a train consisting of a baggage car and a locomotive to go up there to the scene of the wreck. They had young boys going around to the doctors' offices and trying to get miners that had first-aid experience, first-aid crewmen, and any National Guard men that could be of assistance.

We only had the three doctors in town then and I remember thinking when I got on the train, they had two of the doctors, but I didn't see Sam Merritt. "Where is Sam Merritt?" I asked myself. Well, I could have saved my breath, because when we reached the scene of the wreck, Sam was there already. But I'll tell you this much. At first I couldn't recognize him. And I'll leave it to your imagination what his face was covered with that I couldn't recognize him.

How did Sam Merritt get there? How did he happen to be the first there? The first doctor? Well, it's a good question, but tonight we can ask ourselves how Sam Merritt was often the first one to be there, on the scene when he was needed. I'm not taking anything from the other two doctors we had then, or any we had since, but I never knew a man like Sam Merritt for being there when he was needed.

Well, I took a look at Sam and he took a look at me, and then he put me to work. I wasn't a reporter. I was an orderly, or a nurse. There was nobody standing around

that night, taking notes. He worked us all so hard that we hardly got any chance to show any signs of weakness. I tell you what the only thing I can compare it to that I ever saw was, and that was a field hospital. Or more like a dressing station before you got to the field hospital. We got other help from Johnsville, and also from Singerstown and Mountain View and Holtz's and Singers Crossing, and by the time it was dark, some of the doctors and nurses from Gibbsville and Fort Penn, but the commander in chief was Sam Merritt, and we'll never know how many miners had their lives saved because Sam was on the scene so quickly after it happened.

Later on, weeks later, I happened to think of that and I asked Sam, I said, "How did you happen to get there so soon the evening of the wreck?" And do you know what his answer was? His answer was typical, I mean typical of how a doctor can never call his time his own. He said he had a new 16-gauge, a Fox I remember it was, 16-gauge Fox in the back of his tin lizzie and he'd been meaning for days to take it out and fire a few rounds just to get the feel of it, and this particular day he decided that he'd put it off long enough and he was going to fire that gun no matter whose baby didn't get delivered or who got the croup.

So he took the back road out by Schwarzwald's and was looking for a place to stop and get in a little shooting and suddenly he heard the crash. It was suppertime almost, but he had no trouble locating the crash because the boiler blew up and the rear car caught fire. Right away he guessed what happened. Back went the new gun and Sam drove as near as he could to the scene of the wreck and went the rest on foot. And just to show you that the world isn't full of men like Sam Merritt, somebody stole the new gun from the back of the Ford. While he was tending to the injured and dying, somebody went up to his car and stole the shotgun out of the back seat of the car and he never laid eyes on it again.

Well, maybe some of you good people are wondering a little about this speech of mine, if you can call it a speech, so I guess I better tell you how it all happened. I think everybody, or at least everybody from town, all know that Sam Merritt is my best friend and has been since we were boys together. As boys we weren't too close. We didn't get along very well. I never thought much of him and he never thought much of me, but there weren't so many boys the same age, so there was only the four or five white boys and two colored that played together then, and Sam and I were in that bunch. We all used to go out the Glen swimming, or get chased off coal cars and empty freights, and sometimes get caught stealing apples out of Mrs. Fiddler's orchard. Hallowe'en we used to take gates off people's fences, and hold ticktacks up against their windows, or chalk up their sidewalks—where there were sidewalks—or barns, if they didn't have any sidewalks.

Lyons was a great deal different then than it is now, when we were boys. When we were boys they didn't have any radio or television and Sol Pollock hadn't even started up his movie house. You could count the automobiles on the fingers of one hand, and the hose company didn't have the combination truck they have now. We had a hand pumper that we also pulled by hand, or the firemen did. We just ran along after them. I heard my nephew talking the other day about the bucket brigade, as if a bucket brigade was something typical of the Revolutionary War. Well, they had them in the Revolutionary War, but they had them in my time, too, and I don't go back quite that far.

Oh, there were a great many things we have now that we didn't have then, like paved streets, and sidewalks on every street in town. But I can tell you a few things we had then that we don't have now and one of them is trees. You wouldn't know it now, but almost every house in Lyons had its tree in front of it, and sometimes two, and I know in our back yard we had four apple trees and two oxheart cherry trees and two or maybe three sickle pears and a grape arbor.

We have this modern hotel where we are having this banquet this evening, but where this hotel stands there used to be the old Exchange Hotel run by Martin Angstadt, and I can remember him how he used to get very angry if a man's horse chewed the bark off one of the trees in front of his hotel. It meant there was something wrong with the horse but Martin didn't care about the horse. All he cared about was what they were doing to his trees. All I have to do is shut my eyes and remember how Lyons looked thirty, forty years ago when we still had trees. Now instead of trees we have parking meters on Main Street and Market Street and very few trees anywheres else.

But I started to tell you good people how I

happened to be making this speech this evening. I didn't ask to do it, I guarantee you that. But when we began talking among ourselves about giving a banquet in honor of Sam Merritt we had several discussions about asking somebody prominent like the Governor or maybe some famous doctor or somebody like that. But the more we thought of it the more we wanted to make it what you might call a family party. You won't find anybody here tonight that's a stranger to Sam Merritt. We're all either his friends or related to him, and that includes those from out of town that you heard earlier this evening.

We could have got the Governor to come here this evening and you'll notice on the program you'll see printed the names of former Lyons boys that left Lyons and went out to become successful in New York City, Philadelphia, Detroit, Michigan, and other distant places. They all wanted to take some part in the celebration, as Cy told you earlier, so we very graciously permitted them to buy tickets for the dinner even if they couldn't be here to eat it. But we decided that if we got somebody like the Governor it would make it a different kind of a party. Sam Merritt was never one that was much for show and I doubt if he would have permitted us to hold this dinner if it got too elaborate. In fact he said so. If we wanted to hold a banquet for him it had to be kept simple and confined to Lyons people and a few from out of town that he himself would like to have present.

Well, you can't have a party like this without there being a speaker, and the more we went ahead with the preparations the more I noticed that they didn't say anything about who the speaker was going to be. Then finally about two weeks ago I brought it up at a meeting of the committee and the other fellows looked at each other and laughed and I think it was Reese Evans said to me, "Bert, you're it."

"Me?" I said.

"That's right. You. Bert Shoemaker."

"But the dinner's only about two weeks off," I said. I said, "I can't go to work and prepare a speech in two weeks."

"We know that," said Reese. "That's why we didn't tell you before. We don't want a speech. If you prepare a speech it'll be formal and stiff. All we want you to do is stand up on your two feet and kind of reminisce about Sam. You're his best friend and you know him better than anybody else and you won't spill all over with sentimental hogwash."

"That you can be sure of," I said. "Because if I did the first person to leave the room would be Samuel G. Merritt, M.D." So that's how I happened to get picked as the speaker. They allowed me to write down a few notes that I could refer to in case I got stuck for something to say, but that's all. I have these notes here, and just let me hold them up for you to see and you'll readily understand that I wasn't allowed to do much preparation.

So far I haven't referred to my notes but I think I ought to start touching on some of the highlights and I notice I have written down here the word *Family*. I had the experience the other day where there were these two young fellows in their early thirties and one of them made a disparaging remark about the other and I said to him it was no way to talk about his cousin. His cousin? he said. Well, believe it or not, this one young fellow didn't know he was a cousin of the other and it was up to me to explain the relationship. They don't seem to care so much about that any more, and that being the case, I wouldn't be surprised if half the people in this room, especially the younger ones, don't know a great deal about Sam's family history.

Not that I intend to give you a whole family tree, but for their benefit, Sam was born right here in Lyons in the year 1887. His father was Isaac Merritt and Isaac was born here too. Here I have to look at my notes and it says Isaac was born 1860. Eighteen sixty. Well, that was ninety-five years ago, almost a hundred years ago. Mr. Merritt went through school here, first public and then high, then I understand he took the two-year commercial course at Fort Penn Commercial Institute.

What Mr. Merritt's father, Sam's grandfather did, I don't know and I should have found that out before getting up here and talking. However, I do know the family originally came here from Connecticut by way of York State, and I understand the road they have called the Merritt Parkway was named after some family connection, although you'll have to verify that with Sam as that's only my impression and I don't want to make a positive statement to that effect. But that's what the stock was. New England. Then in 1883 Sam's father married Miss Frieda Langendorf, and the Langendorfs are an old Lyons family, which most of you know. The Langendorfs built the first trolley

line here and I guess there wasn't much accomplished around here that the Langendorfs didn't have something to do with.

Sam was the second son of that union. He had an older brother, Isaac Junior, known as Boo for some reason I couldn't fathom. Boo Merritt was always known as Boo even in the privacy of the home. Boo received an appointment to the United States Naval Academy at Annapolis, Maryland, and he was in his third year there doing extremely well when he contracted spinal meningitis and passed away at the age of twenty. He was the tallest of the Merritt family and some said he grew too fast. That may be, but I can tell you all the girls fell for him when he came home on vacation in his Annapolis midshipman's uniform. In those days we used to have a dance at Christmas at the Odd Fellows Hall and the rest of us weren't in it when Boo was around.

Boo passing away was very hard on Sam not only because they were very close for two brothers about the same age, but also he had the responsibility of being the oldest of the Merritt children. There was Victoria, now Mrs. J. J. Singer, and Dorothy, Mrs. D. W. Schleicher, of Johnsville, both ladies it is my pleasure to see here tonight observing the affair in honor of their older brother. Then there was Oscar Merritt, Sam's younger brother, born 1891 and passed away at the age of six of typhoid, so I guess you couldn't call him a responsibility when Boo died, although naturally Mr. and Mrs. Merritt must have thought back to their early loss when Boo died, and that was a sort of a responsibility for Sam.

I often think it was Boo that decided Sam to become a doctor. When he passed away, that is. Up to then I don't remember Sam ever saying much about being a doctor. This is only what I think, but when we were young boys together I would have said Sam would grow up to be a carpenter. Carpenter and builder. In those days a master carpenter could build a house and all the help he needed was an apprentice, and by the time Sam was fourteen or fifteen years of age, he was the handiest with tools in our bunch, and one summer when he was fifteen or sixteen, he put in new shelves and bins and one counter in his father's store. He did it all by himself.

Today I guess Sam has the best amateur carpentry shop in town down in the cellar at his house, and a lot of us here tonight have articles of furniture that Sam made in his own shop, just for pleasure. Very fine workmanship, too. Not only articles of furniture, but also the gavel they use at Rotary, that was made by Sam. The pulpit at the M. E. church, that was made by Sam, not to mention countless cigar humidors and things for the ladies to keep their sewing in.

I often heard Sam say he could make more cash money as a carpenter than as a doctor, because people pay their carpenter before they pay their doctor, but I promised I wouldn't say anything about that tonight because I don't think anybody'd have the nerve to show their face here tonight if they owed Sam for an unpaid bill. I wouldn't think of mentioning that, because I don't think anybody'd drive here in a nice new sedan if they still owed Sam for medical attention a year or two ago. So I won't say anything about that.

Nobody has to make excuses for not paying Sam the money they owe him, because Sam makes up their excuses himself. I remember saying to him some years ago, I said I noticed that a certain family were sending their son away to college and they seemed to forget they owed Sam over eight hundred dollars. "Well," said Sam, "eight hundred dollars will only pay for one semester and if the boy's no good and flunks out at the end of the one semester, that'll be a heartache for the parents. And if the boy finishes and makes a good showing, I'll get some satisfaction out of knowing that I helped put him through." That's the kind of story that everybody here can tell about Sam Merritt.

I used to try to persuade him to leave his money at home when he went out on his calls because if he had twenty-five dollars in his pocket when he went out, that was no guarantee that he was going to have twenty-five when he got home. And don't forget, friends, some of his patients used to pay him cash by the visit.

"At least don't give away more than you earn in a day," I used to say to him. But Sam would take a look at some poor family and how they were living, or existing, and before he got home that evening he'd have an order of groceries and meat and clothes for the children on their way to the poor family.

Not that the poor weren't grateful. It wasn't the poor he should have worried about. I guess if there's one man here to-

night that knows more about that than I do it's Reverend Smirnolinski, because he had more poor people in his parish than the other denominations. If you want to know what the Irish think of Sam Merritt you ought to take a look at some of the embroidery tablecloths and napkins the Sisters made for the Merritt family. And don't think that makes Sam any the less a good Methodist, because it doesn't. Sam's a good Mason and I don't have to say any more on that subject because I just got the signal to pipe down, but I think you all got my meaning.

I was saying a minute ago that when he was a young fellow in his teens, I didn't think Sam Merritt would ever be a doctor. I never even gave it a thought. Take high school. In botany he was all right, but when he had biology Sam would turn green when he had to dissect a frog. As far as any of us know, there was never a doctor in the Merritt or the Langendorf family, and the nearest thing to it was I understand the Merritt store did a thriving business in Peruna. That was a medicine that you didn't need a prescription for and it cured all your aches and pains. Some people took Peruna that wouldn't per-

mit you to mention the name of Old Over-
holt, but the one made you feel just as good
as the other.

One summer Sam got a job tending the
soda fountain at Brown's but he didn't learn
anything about medicine that summer. I had
the same job another summer and we used
to close at half past nine, but it was always
near eleven before I got home by the time I
got finished washing the soda glasses and ice-
cream dishes and packing down those cans
with ice and mixing syrup for the next day.
Nobody had time to learn anything on that
job. Except how smart old Doc Brown was,
hiring a young fellow that thought he was
going to gorge himself on ice cream and paying him two dollars a week and working him
so hard he didn't even have time to eat up
the profits.

But I'm not up here to pay compliments to
old Doc Brown and his business ability. You
wanted somebody to take a cinder out of your
eye, Doc was as efficient at that as any professional man. Or, a little indigestion, Doc
would give you a glass of soda water, or somebody'd faint and they'd be revived in Doc
Brown's drugstore. In fact, Brown's drugstore in those days was the closest we had to

a hospital here in Lyons. The collieries had shacks where injured men would be taken and put in bed till it was time to move them to the hospital in Fort Penn. But if there was a runaway horse and somebody got hurt, or for instance somebody fell on the ice and broke a leg, if it happened anywhere near Doc Brown's drugstore, that's where they'd take him.

And all those things meant expense to old Doc and usually there wasn't anybody to send a bill to, not to mention who had to clean up the drugstore after an accident. In a way Doc Brown should be here tonight, because although he didn't start Sam Merritt to becoming a doctor, I know that when Sam finally did go away to medical college, when he came home for vacation he always used to sit and talk to Doc Brown in those two big easy chairs Doc had in the back of the drugstore.

Doc would sit there in one of those big easy chairs and without getting up he could see who was in the store, and usually he could guess what they wanted. I guess a lot of people used to wonder how Doc Brown would know they were in the store. Well, I'll tell you. He had a peephole. It wasn't a regular peephole, such as they have in the curtain

on a theatrical stage. Doc's peephole was this
way: there was a row of medicine bottles on a
shelf that stood between the store proper and
the back room. Well, there was an empty
place in that row of bottles and from where
he sat Doc could sit in the chair and see
through that vacant place and watch the people come in the front door.

I remember one time when I was about
fourteen years old, I went in the store and
Doc was in the back and I didn't think he
heard me. So I reached down in the cigar
counter and helped myself to two Philadelphia Hand-Mades and stuck them in my
pocket. Then I called out, "Anybody here?"
and Doc came out and waited on me. I guess
I was getting something for my mother or
father, and whatever it was, I said to charge
it, and Doc said to me, "Want me to put the
cigars on the bill or will you pay for them
yourself? Since when did your father start
smoking cigars?"

Well, I guess Doc Brown and Sam Merritt
had many an interesting chat after Sam
started going to medical college. I noticed
since then that other Lyons boys that went
away to study medicine used to drop in and
loaf around at Doc Brown's. One way of

keeping in touch with the profession and learning about prescriptions. Even after they got their degree they used to be in Doc Brown's till they got started building up a practice, although in a town like Lyons there was always plenty of work for a doctor if he didn't care when he got paid. I guess that's the same everywhere, not only Lyons.

The older men, the established ones, they got so much a year being company doctor at one of the collieries, and so much for various lodges, and usually the Protestant doctors got all the Protestants and the Catholic doctor got all the Catholics, and one of the older doctors would get the Reading Railway and the other would get the Pennsy. What was left for the young fellow just starting out was pretty slim pickings and some of it we don't have to talk about in mixed company. I know this much, that in 1915, when Sam Merritt hung out his shingle, I was getting eighteen a week working for my father on the old *Republican* and Sam was Dr. Samuel G. Merritt, or Dr. S. G. Merritt, I was a married man with a wife and daughter and Sam didn't feel he could afford to get married yet. Of course I didn't have to have my own tin lizzie and buy surgical instruments and things like that.

Surgical instruments. I want to ask Sam Merritt here and now, yes or no, is it true what I heard thirty-five or more years ago that one day he and four or five other fellows were out gunning for deer out in the Valley and they spent the night at a farmhouse out there and the farmer was putting in new timbers in the barn and somehow or other a big stone block fell on him and crushed his foot and they couldn't get the stone off. Now what I want to know, tonight after all these years, is it true that Sam cut off the foot with an ordinary handsaw? Sam says yes, he's nodding to me. That's all I wanted to know. I've been waiting thirty-five years for the answer to that, but Sam would never tell me. I don't know why. If you can do as good a job—well, some of the ladies don't appear to be very pleased with this kind of talk, so I'll change the subject.

Perhaps it would be more fitting if I went back to what I was saying about Boo Merritt and how when he passed away it decided Sam to be a doctor. Up to then Sam wouldn't even help out if a mare was having a colt, and I told you how he felt about dissecting. I'll tell you this much too, and I don't think it will make anybody sick. Sam Merritt the first

time he ever saw a real operation fainted. He
told me that himself. That was at the Jeffer-
son Medical College in Philadelphia and he
just keeled over. He got used to it, but the
first time, he and I think two other students
fell flat on their faces. Well, a man that wanted to be a doctor that bad must have had
some underlying reason for it, and according
to the way I look at it, Sam was so incensed
over what happened to Boo that he began
to wonder or say to himself, "If I can prevent
that, it's my job to prevent it."

Why do I say that? Well, I don't think Sam
said it in so many words. But if you look at
Sam's whole career as a doctor and as a man,
I never saw anybody like Sam for wanting to
right a wrong. A doctor is always righting
wrongs. That's his business, or profession, if
you prefer. He is supposed to cure people,
which is the same thing as righting a wrong.
But now there was brother Boo, passing away
just when he ought to be starting life. I don't
say Sam resolved to find a cure for spinal
meningitis, nothing like that. But Boo passing away just showed Sam that there was a
way he could right wrongs and make it his
lifework.

Maybe when Oscar passed away that had

49

something to do with it, but by the time Boo passed away Sam was a little older and more likely to think about such things. Up to then Sam was destined to be a carpenter, if the signs meant anything, but shortly after Boo passed away Sam began taking an interest in doctoring and have long talks with Dr. George Steever, and there is a man that ought to be here tonight to give us the full story of how Sam finally made his decision, because if it hadn't of been for Dr. George Steever, in my opinion Sam never would have gone to medical college.

Looking around, my guess is that Dr. George Steever is responsible for over half the people in this room. Those he didn't personally bring into the world, he brought one or both of their parents. In my case he brought me into the world and Sam Merritt and all Sam's brothers and sisters. But they gave Dr. Steever a celebration years ago when he retired to St. Petersburg, Florida, and this party is for Sam Merritt. But it wouldn't be complete if I didn't mention the late Dr. George Steever. He used to let Sam go along with him on his calls and that way Sam got a first-hand look at what it would be like to be a doctor, and of course we have to give Dr.

Steever credit for recognizing Sam's ability.
Or maybe not ability, because Sam didn't
have any ability then, but Dr. Steever had
the insight to realize that Sam would make a
good doctor and helped him get into medical
college and also convinced Mr. Isaac Merritt
that it was worth going to all that expense. I
just remember now that I made a note of
Dr. Steever and here I mentioned him without consulting my notes.

Well, since I took a look at my notes I
might as well take a good look at them and
see what I have down here. *Hobbies*. I guess
if you didn't know it before you know it
now, that Sam always liked to go gunning.
That was one hobby I wouldn't be surprised
if Sam brought down as many as fifteen deer
in the space of thirty years. That's nothing
unusual in Lyons, but I'll bet some of you
will be surprised to hear that Sam was I think
the last man to get a bear in this town. I
mean by that, within ten miles of town. I
haven't even heard of a bear being seen the
last twenty years, but there were still some in
the woods on Klinger's Mountain as late as
1916, the year Sam got his. That's still pretty
wild country through there but I never heard
of anybody from town getting a bear since

Sam shot his. What would that be? Thirty-five years ago. I mean thirty-nine. Thank you.

Sam hardly ever took a real vacation but there was one day he kept sacred and that was the opening day of the hunting season, even if all he went out for was pheasants. If he ever came back with an empty pouch I never heard of it, because Sam was a very good shot with gun or rifle. A little better with the shotgun because he got more practice, but he was what I call a hunting shooter. Some of our fellows out at the Gun Club could beat Sam shooting blue rocks or target, but when you got out in the woods or out where there was quail, Sam didn't miss very many. He had a lot of patience. I don't mean that the way you took it. I meant the other kind of patience, not p-a-t-i-e-n-t-s. He had both kinds, but the kind of patience I have reference to is the kind whereby you can wait and wait for hours, if necessary. If Sam was convinced there was deer in a certain locality, he'd stand there like a statue till he got a shot at the animal. Sam could stand there with a chew of tobacco in his mouth and never move a muscle. Maybe I shouldn't have said that about chewing tobacco. But Sam chewed all his life and half the time I wouldn't know if he had a chew in or not. Most people didn't know he even chewed. Well, I guess that about covers gunning.

Carpentry I already spoke of. This do-it-yourself craze you hear so much about nowadays, Sam was ahead of the public by forty years. Other hobbies I won't mention because a Methodist isn't supposed to play cards. Well, anybody that ever played bridge or poker with a certain friend of ours, he didn't violate any religious scruples with the kind of bridge and poker he played. All I can say is that if Methodists aren't supposed to play bridge or poker, this friend of ours played like a Methodist.

Maybe the true test of how fond we are of this man is that I noticed there are several people in this room, myself among them, and anybody that speaks to him, let alone attends a banquet for him, must be very fond of him after being his partner at a game of bridge. Suffice it to say that he went right on playing auction after everybody else in the country was playing contract. They tell the famous story of the fellow that was playing bridge one time and after he got set five tricks doubled and redoubled and vulnerable, his partner said to him, "Herman, when did you learn to play bridge? Don't just say today, say what time today." That fits our friend to the letter. Yes, our friend had to have a lot of lovable qualities to overcome his lack of ability when it came to playing cards.

Earlier in this talk, or remarks, or whatever you wish to call them, I spoke of Sam Merritt's service to the community. In my opinion it would have been enough just to have Sam Merritt attending to our aches and pains, great or small, and carrying us through our illnesses, major or minor. The majority of us here tonight have felt the touch of his hand on our pulse or had him tell us to say "Ah" and do all the things a family doctor does in the course of his daily routine. Old or young, rich or poor, we all felt better for having Sam in charge because we had the confidence that with Sam there beside us and looking after us, we had more than a doctor there. We had if not a friend—those that did not know him on that basis—we had the instinctive feeling that here was a man that the thing he wanted most in the world was for us to get well, and if there was anything in his power, he'd see to it that we did.

I look around and see a lot of you nodding

in agreement. Yes, so many of us have shared that experience in our acquaintance with Sam. Speaking from personal experience, he saved my life on two separate occasions. Once when I had pneumonia and the other time was when we were both about twenty and out swimming at the Glen I got cramps and it was Sam that not only pulled me out but brought me to. Many of the young people he brought into the world went out and served their country in Africa, Europe, the Pacific and Korea, and there are children in this town tonight that Sam not only delivered them but also both of their parents. Some of us are walking around with both legs or have the use of both hands that if it hadn't of been for Sam's care we would have been minus a limb. In all our memories as long as we live we'll all have some reason to be grateful to Sam Merritt. And it ought to be a great satisfaction to Sam, although the kind of man Sam is, I don't even think he gives that a thought. He would only consider that he had done his duty according to the oath of I am sorry to say I can't recall the name of the famous Greek person that made up the oath that all doctors are supposed to take.

But as though that were not sufficient to

make an indelible impression on the history of our community, let us not, my friends, overlook his service to the community as a whole and not merely what we know and recall as individuals. For Samuel G. Merritt made a contribution to this community that is not generally known and to the best of my knowledge and belief, never was given credit for. Perhaps many of you, even those who hold him in high esteem and consider that you are his friends, perhaps many of you will be hearing this for the first time.

Now I see our friend frowning at me because he is beginning to suspect the nature of what I am about to tell you and he would vastly prefer that I maintain silence on the subject. But this is a family party in which I see nobody here that does not belong here. This is a family party and I was delegated to make the principal address because I happen to be the guest of honor's best friend. Therefore in spite of the silent protest of our guest of honor, I consider it my duty at least once and for all to relate to you the true story of a service which he rendered the community that many of us are apt to overlook and many others do not even know about.

Sam, you're just going to have to sit there

and let me talk, so stop making faces at me.

Back in the middle of the nineteen twenties, and all the years preceding, if somebody from Lyons had to have a major operation or hospital care, they had their choice of two hospitals. The person could go to Gibbsville, thirty-five miles away, or they could go to Fort Penn, a distance of forty-four miles. Most people preferred to go to Fort Penn because although Gibbsville was nearer by nine miles, it meant mountain travel all the way, whereas Fort Penn meant there was only one mountain between Lyons and there.

In the old days when I was a boy the only ambulance we had was owned by the colliery and it was drawn by mules. If a miner got badly hurt in the mines they would bring him first to the first-aid shack and then put him in the ambulance and put him in the baggage car of the Pennsy train, the morning one or the evening one, and I don't have to tell you that half the time by the time the train was ready to leave, the injured man was beyond all assistance on this earth.

Later on the collieries had an automobile ambulance, but even that wasn't much of an improvement in bad weather. The roads from here to Gibbsville were usually drifted, or the tires would go bad, or that old Winton would get engine trouble and there they'd be stuck halfway between here and Gibbsville till somebody came along and pulled them out. From here to Fort Penn was better, but not all that better.

Well, then came the great influenza epidemic of 1918 and the people around here were dying like flies. Odd Fellows Hall was turned into an emergency hospital and so was the Moose Hall. Sam and other doctors used to work till they dropped and then they'd have a cup of coffee and start working some more. But all those conditions convinced Sam that we needed a hospital here in Lyons. Thirty-five miles away, forty-four miles away was too far to take somebody that was dying of illness or accident. So that was when Sam began his one-man campaign to raise funds for a hospital here in Lyons.

You know what the first thing he did was, after he got an estimate on how much the hospital would cost? He put up all his savings, a little over $14,000, mortgaged his house for another ten thousand, got his mother to donate a thousand, and he was in business. In other words, he was able to go

around to people and say he had raised $25,000 toward a new hospital for Lyons.

The lowest estimate he could get for the completely equipped small hospital, completely equipped but with nothing fancy, was $300,000. So he went to his sisters and got between them another five thousand, and that way he was able to tell people that ten per cent of the cost was already raised. He didn't bother to tell anybody that all the money had been raised inside his own family, mostly by Sam himself. Some of you easily remember what a campaign he put on. First he started with his friends, and he bled us dry, but we were only too glad. All you had to do was listen to Sam giving his sales talk and he made it seem like a pleasure to dig down in your pocket or your bank account and give till it hurt and then give some more, as they used to say. The other two doctors in town put up five thousand apiece and more credit to them, because it was a lot of money in those days.

Of course everywhere Sam went to collect money or pledges, everybody said what about the coal companies? Why don't you get the money from them? But Sam said he was more anxious to have it a community enterprise first and save the coal companies for big contributions later, when more than half the money was raised and the coal companies couldn't say no. The same with the Union. Sam felt that if Lyons raised most of the money, the Union and the operators would be practically forced into putting up the balance.

Well, Sam was doing fine, pleading and persuading and badgering. All the town churches had euchres and bake sales and sold chances on this or that, and Rotary and Kiwanis and the fraternal oragnizations all chipped in, and Sam added up one day and realized that he had in money and pledges just a little over $200,000. Now was the time to go to the coal companies and the Union!

Then the ax fell.

The day before he was going to call on the coal companies the miners went out on strike. That turned out to be a strike lasting from the first of September, '25, to the twelfth of February, '26. What a winter that was. Men standing around with nothing to do and no colliery whistles sounding in the hills, everybody short on rations or going to soup kitchens, and merchants wondering if they'd be able to stay open much longer. And who

was the most unpopular man in Lyons? Not the superintendent, not the district leader of the Union. No, the most unpopular man was Sam Merritt, because he held onto the cash he had collected and wouldn't give it back. He knew if he gave it back it would be twice as hard to collect again and he held onto it in two special accounts at the two town banks.

I am proud to confess that I gave one fellow a punch in the jaw right out in the middle of Main Street when he hinted that the strike didn't worry Sam Merritt with all that money in the bank. And there was a lot of that kind of talk that I didn't hear first-hand or I would have had to give a few more socks in the jaw. I happened to know that the only meat Sam had in the house during the whole month of December was some venison he shot, and likewise he only had enough heat in the house to warm the first floor where the office was. I think a lot of people went to that office that didn't have much wrong with them but only wanted to keep warm.

Well, the strike was settled on Lincoln's Birthday and Sam and I had a little drink of schnapps to celebrate the occasion and he said he was going to go back to work. "Back to work?" I said.

"Back collecting for the hospital," he said. And so he did. Inside of a week he was around getting a few pledges, then he tackled the coal companies. He got twenty thousand apiece from the two independents, but then when he went and called on the Nesquehela he got nothing but a cold stare.

"Why not?" he said.

"We have other plans," they said.

"Well, let me in on the plans. I've raised most of the money. It's all in the town banks. Every penny accounted for. It didn't cost a cent to collect the money, but we can't start to build without your contribution. We need seventy-five thousand." Sam pleaded with them.

"We have other plans," was all they'd say.

Then about two days later Sam had a visitor. Call him Dr. Blank. He's a blank as far as I'm concerned. He came into Sam's office and said, "Doctor, naturally we've been hearing a lot about your little hospital, or at least your plans for a little hospital."

Sam said yes, and to go ahead.

"Well," the other doctor said, "we've been having the same idea up in Johnsville."

"Oh, you have, have you?" said Sam.

"When did you first get your idea?"

"Well, when we got the idea doesn't make any difference. The point is we've raised some money too because we want the hospital to be in Johnsville."

"Why not Lyons? We've been working on this for a year," said Sam.

"Yes, but you've gone as far as you can without the contribution from Nesquehela."

"That's true," said Sam. "Why don't you come in with us and we'll have a Lyons-Johnsville hospital. We can go ahead without Nesquehela."

"Ah, but we have Nesquehela, and we want the hospital for Johnsville."

Sam picked up the phone and called the super and asked if it was true that Nesquehela was backing Johnsville. Yes, he was told, it was true. "And I suppose Dr. Blank is to be superintendent of the new Johnsville Hospital?" said Sam. Yes, that was true.

"All right, Doctor, you'll hear from me," said Sam.

I don't know what must have gone on in Sam's mind the next few hours, but I know that he sat down and wrote a letter that we printed and sent to every single person and organization that had contributed to the

Lyons Hospital campaign. I could quote you the whole letter but what's the use. It explained what had happened, that Johnsville was also planning a hospital and had been promised the Nesquehela contribution, without which Lyons could not start to build. He then urged all who had contributed to the Lyons hospital to authorize him to turn the contribution over to Johnsville, because it would mean a much bigger and better-equipped institution, and after all Johnsville was only eight miles away.

Sam worded that letter so carefully that most people were convinced that it was their duty to turn the money over to Johnsville, and over 85 per cent of them did. And this is something that nobody ever knew before tonight—namely, that included in the money that Johnsville got was the $30,000 that Sam raised inside his own family.

That's the kind of man we honor here tonight.

Now I hope Sam forgives me for telling that story. I know he won't hold it against me, because if Sam was the kind of a man that held things against people, that story never would have happened and I wouldn't be telling it tonight. I know this much: I

would not have forgiven myself if I hadn't
come out with the true facts on why Johnsville has a hospital and Lyons doesn't. And I
could tell by the way you good people ap-
plauded that many of you were hearing it
for the first time, and that does my heart
good. I don't know of a better story that
illustrates the bigness of Sam Merritt, a bigger man than his own personal, professional
disappointment, bigger than envy, bigger
than mere personal pride. No one would
have blamed Sam for getting out of the hospital deal and withdrawing his support, no
one would have been disappointed in Sam.
But I'll tell you, my friends, I think we
would have been surprised. It was no surprise
when he gave the Johnsville Hospital his support, not to mention his money. What would
have been a surprise was if he had acted in any
other way, because the finest principles is
what we take for granted when we think of
Sam Merritt. . . .

And now I come to the part of Sam's life
that we all make the mistake of pretending
it did not exist and therefore, in my opinion,
make it worse than it really is. This is a
family party and every person in this room is
a member of a family and every family has

its family secrets. Or so we think, that they are secrets. Yet I say with no hesitation that there is not a man or woman here this evening who has not at some time during the course of the evening said to himself or herself, "How sad that Alice cannot be with us tonight."

You look at me, some of you, as if to say, "Haven't you got sense enough to avoid certain topics? Do you have to speak of Alice tonight of all nights?" I say to you in reply, to pretend to ignore the subject of Alice would be hypocritical to the nth degree. And worse than that, if I got up here and talked about Sam without talking about Alice would be as wrong as if I did not mention Dr. George Steever and the part he played in Sam's medical career, or the sadness that came to Sam when his brother Boo died. And the worst thing of all, I would be cruelly unfair to Alice herself. Yes, unfair to Alice.

I know what is going on in some minds, but I do not agree. We have now been here since half past seven, a good three hours, and yet I have not heard anyone mention Alice by name. Why? Alice is not dead. We all know that. But if I don't risk the displeasure and disapproval of a few, this evening would

pass without mentioning her and it would be as though Alice had never existed. And how dishonest and false that would be.

Do some of you think that by not mentioning Alice I would be sparing Sam? If you do, then you don't know the man as I know him. For there is never a minute of the day when Alice is not in his thoughts. And believe me, my friends, if we ignored Alice tonight, I don't think we would earn Sam's gratitude. I know Sam Merritt and I know that when he finally went home tonight, after he turned out the light and was alone with his thoughts and mulling over the events of the evening, I know that he would wish that someone, someone had found the words to express some appreciation for the one person, the one person who more than anybody else in the world was responsible for the position Sam Merritt occupies in our community and in our hearts.

They have a saying that they use nowadays and like so many sayings, they think it's a new one. But it isn't. We used to say it when we were young fellows and girls. It is the expression "going steady." Young people were going steady forty, fifty years ago. It is that long ago that Sam Merritt began going steady with Alice Connor. In fact, Sam started going steady with Alice when he was in high and she was still in grammar because they had the three years' difference in their ages.

Some parents, like today, did not approve of their daughters going steady so early and Mr. and Mrs. Connor were among them. But with Alice it was Sam or nobody and it was the same with Sam. Mr. and Mrs. Connor had nothing against Sam, but they naturally didn't want her to get serious when they were only in high school. Therefore they had a talk with Sam about it and in a friendly way they told him that they thought Alice should be given the chance to get better acquainted with other boys.

But they soon found out that their daughter had no interest in other boys. Luckily they were sensible people and accepted the verdict but they would not allow the young couple to become engaged until Sam finished medical college. Then it was delayed because Sam was interning at a hospital in Philadelphia and then delayed some more while he was getting started. They finally felt they were in a position to get married and I was given the honor of being best man. Now I

don't believe there's anybody in this room that would be such a damn fool as to think that I would say anything that would injure Sam Merritt. I was his best man, he was my best man, and next to my own wife Lou there was never a girl that I revered more than Alice Connor.

They got married and the early years of struggle were happy ones because they were practically the one person. Alice didn't take the training course to be a nurse, but she learned it all. She learned bookkeeping in high, so she was able to keep Sam's books for him. In addition she did all the housework herself and when Sam began doing a little better financially and tried to persuade her to get a hired girl, she said she would rather use the money for some other purpose, such as a new car, or office furniture, or for the new additions to the family. Unfortunately, both times they were expecting, they lost both babies. One died at birth and the other was premature.

Alice was terribly disappointed when the babies did not live but it did not deter her from going right on working to assist Sam in his professional career. But without realizing it, her strength must have been more seriously affected than anyone realized, and soon after that she began to show signs that after the second baby she had not made a complete recovery. She was subject to depression and after a time Sam took her to the best doctors in Fort Penn and they examined her and recommended a complete rest in a private hospital near Fort Penn.

When she came home she was all right for a while, but the old trouble returned and once again Sam accompanied her to Fort Penn. Only a few of their closest friends knew about her condition at the time. We used the excuse that Alice was having a series of operations. The second time she came home from the private hospital Sam brought a trained nurse back and we all made believe that the nurse was there to help Sam in the office, but then I guess the truth got to be known publicly when what we all know happened. One of her moods of depression and she jumped out of the second-story window. Broke both her legs, one arm.

We all know about it. It happened in broad daylight, people walking in the street. I never saw the use of any secrecy after that. As long as there was a chance of recovery, yes. But by the next day it was no more a

secret in Lyons than if the borough hall
caught fire and burned down. We didn't run
anything in the *Republican* about it, but I
often thought since then that it would have
been better for all concerned if we had. Maybe we would have put a stop to all the idle
rumors that circulated.

Well, that was a long time ago, a long time
ago. Some twenty-five years, and a little more.
We're all getting on. What Alice looks like
today, I don't know. But what I do know is
how I prefer to think of her, slender, light
brown hair, devoted to the only man she ever
cared for, working with him, encouraging
him until she was no longer able to. Now
they have operations that they can cure the
kind of illness Alice had, but they didn't
have them then and they don't advise it now.

Well, I've brought it out in the open and
it isn't a happy story, of course, but would
anybody be any the happier if I didn't mention the only woman that Sam ever loved,
the woman that loved him? That helped him
when he needed help the most? Friends, I
don't think anybody, Alice or Sam or anybody, was hurt by any of this, and maybe
somebody was even helped.

In fact, I can be sure of that. I don't have

to say maybe. Because I have the honor to announce—to you, Sam, because everybody else in this room knows it—that those here tonight have raised the sum of $20,000 for the maternity ward of the Johnsville Hospital, to be known as the Alice C. Merritt Ward. And I take great pleasure in handing you this check, on this engraved silver platter. I will read the engraving:

Presented to
Samuel G. Merritt, M. D.,
at a Family Party in Honor of
His First Forty Years of Service
To His Community.

I thank you.

STEINBECK'S PEOPLE

Jody, Adam Trask, Lennie, Doc—these aren't just names of fictional characters. To anyone who has ever read THE RED PONY, EAST OF EDEN, OF MICE AND MEN, or CANNERY ROW, these are real people.

When John Steinbeck writes about people, they come alive. The reader knows how they look, how they think, how they act and how they feel. He knows all their longings, their lusts, their passions and their innermost secrets. And, he becomes a part of some of the most moving fictional experiences of our time.

TRAVELS WITH CHARLEY 75¢
THE RED PONY 45¢
OF MICE AND MEN 50¢
EAST OF EDEN 95¢
CANNERY ROW 50¢
THE WAYWARD BUS 60¢
THE PEARL 45¢

At your Bantam Book Dealer or Mail Coupon Today